Barry Appleby's

The GAMBOLS

BOOK Nº 47

by
Roger Mahoney

Published by

Pedigree® BOOKS

The Old Rectory
Matford Lane, Exeter
Devon EX2 4PS

Under licence from Express Newspapers plc. Printed in the UK.

£6.99

(GA47)

4

THEY SAY THAT MONEY MAKES THE
WORLD GO ROUND — IT CERTAINLY
MAKES GEORGE'S HEAD SPIN

14

OCCASIONALLY GEORGE SEES THE
FUNNY SIDE OF SHOPPING

16

GAYE THINKS HER FIRM WOULD
COLLAPSE IF EVER SHE LEFT —
HER BOSS FEELS SURE OF IT

29

VIDEOS... COMPUTER GAMES... STEREOS ~
FOR MIGGY AND FLIVVER A WELL STOCKED
REFRIGERATOR IS STILL HIGH ON THEIR
LIST OF PRIORITIES

32

33

GAYE LOVES NOTHING BETTER THAN
TO HELP GEORGE RESTORE THAT
OLD CAR ~ AT LEAST THAT'S WHAT
GEORGE SAYS

GEORGE IS NOT SO MUCH A D.I.Y
ENTHUSIAST — HE'S MORE OF A
D.I.Y DABBLER

44

GAYE CAN ALWAYS SEE THE FUNNY
SIDE OF OFFICE LIFE

49

GARDENING CAN BE A BACK-BREAKING
HOBBY — AS GEORGE KNOWS ONLY TOO WELL

PLANNING THEIR HOLIDAYS TOGETHER
IS ONE OF GEORGE AND GAYES FAVOURITE
PASTIMES

HOLIDAYS ARE GREAT FUN — BUT ALL
TOO SOON WE'RE BACK IN THE OLD
ROUTINE

TROUBLE WITH THE CAR? GEORGE SAYS
A TWIDDLE WITH A SCREWDRIVER WILL
SOLVE ALL PROBLEMS

82

GEORGE LOVES TO TRY HIS HAND AT COOKING — HIS LATEST SPECIALITY IS KITCHEN FLAMBÉ

GENTLE PERSUASION IS THE ONLY WAY THAT
GAYE CAN GET GEORGE TO TAKE EXERCISE

OCCASIONALLY GEORGE INSISTS ON DOING HIS SHARE OF THE HOUSEWORK

AH CHRISTMAS — A TIME
FOR FUN LAUGHTER AND
MERRIMENT

BUT IT'S ALSO LOVELY WHEN LIFE
GETS BACK TO NORMAL

HOW TIME FLIES — HERE WE ARE AT THE
END OF OUR GAMBOLS ANNUAL NUMBER 47 —
BUT WE'LL BE WAITING TO SEE YOU AGAIN
TOMORROW MORNING IN THE EXPRESS
WHERE YOU CAN MEET THE GAMBOLS
EVERY DAY — 'BYE FOR NOW